Why Explore Space?

| asteroid | establish | goals | resolve | suspend |
| demonstrate | galaxy | meteor | retreat | treacherous |

A. From the Word Bank above, choose the word that best matches each meaning. Write the word on the line provided.

1. _____ Filled with potential dangers and hazards

2. _____ The ends toward which you direct your efforts

3. _____ To back off from your position or withdraw from a situation

4. _____ To make a firm decision to do something and be successful

5. _____ To stop temporarily

6. _____ A rock or metal in space that forms a streak of light when it enters Earth's atmosphere

7. _____ A large group of stars and planets in the universe

8. _____ To prove an idea, concept, or theory

9. _____ A rocky or metallic planetary body that circles the Sun

10. _____ To show something clearly, such as knowledge or skill

B. Choose one of the words in the Word Bank above to complete each sentence. Write the word in the line provided.

11. After the other team scored three _____, we became very discouraged.

12. Our cat's usual _____ during a thunderstorm is under the bed.

13. Olivia's parents threatened to _____ her computer privileges if her grades didn't improve.

14. If everyone works together, we may be able to _____ the problem.

15. They thought they saw a _____, but it was only an airplane preparing to land.

C. Fill in the bubble next to the answer that best completes the sentence or answers the question.

16. If you *establish* the facts, you
    ○ **A** question them
    ○ **B** find out what's true
    ○ **C** disprove an idea
    ○ **D** categorize them

17. Read this sentence:
    Science fiction stories often include visitors from another *galaxy.*

    A *galaxy* is
    ○ **A** a solar system
    ○ **B** a universe
    ○ **C** a large group of stars and planets
    ○ **D** a constellation

18. When you set *goals,* you
    ○ **A** prepare for a soccer game
    ○ **B** work to meet a deadline
    ○ **C** plan your weekend
    ○ **D** decide what you want to achieve

19. The opposite of *retreat* is
    ○ **A** withdraw
    ○ **B** advance
    ○ **C** expose
    ○ **D** abandon

20. When you *resolve* an argument, you get the two parties involved to
    ○ **A** come to an agreement
    ○ **B** speak calmly
    ○ **C** explain their positions
    ○ **D** make formal complaints

21. Read this sentence:
    Trying to climb a rock face without the proper equipment is a *treacherous* undertaking.

    Treacherous means
    ○ **A** full of potential danger
    ○ **B** difficult
    ○ **C** testing one's ability
    ○ **D** requiring great skill

22. If you *suspend* your normal activities, you
    ○ **A** continue as usual
    ○ **B** tell people your schedule
    ○ **C** begin your usual routine
    ○ **D** stop your usual routine

23. An *asteroid* is a planetary body that is
    ○ **A** larger than Earth
    ○ **B** in orbit around Earth
    ○ **C** smaller than an actual planet
    ○ **D** formed from garbage in space

24. When you *demonstrate* something, you
    ○ **A** show it clearly
    ○ **B** try to make it work
    ○ **C** learn to operate it
    ○ **D** prove it with facts

25. When a *meteor* enters Earth's atmosphere, it
    ○ **A** forms a streak of light
    ○ **B** returns to space
    ○ **C** turns to rain
    ○ **D** breaks apart

2

Name _____ Date _____ Class _____

The Life Cycle of a Star

bond	combustion	compress	luminous	overall
coincide	compound	comprise	monitor	reaction

A. From the Word Bank above, choose the word that best matches each meaning. Write the word on the line provided.

1. _____ To reduce in size by pushing or squeezing together

2. _____ To watch and keep track of what is happening

3. _____ A strong tie or unifying force or binding element

4. _____ To be made up of

5. _____ When all circumstances are taken in account

6. _____ Shining or glowing

7. _____ To combine or come together to form a whole

8. _____ The act of bursting into flames and burning

9. _____ A change that involves a chemical transformation

10. _____ To happen at the same time

B. Choose one of the words in the Word Bank above to complete each sentence. Write the word on the line provided.

11. Sometimes people _____ the instant they meet and become friends.

12. Bad weather and unpleasant chores can _____ to make a bad day.

13. A lifeguard is a pool _____ whose job is to ensure that all swimmers follow the rules and do not get into danger.

14. She had to sit on the suitcase in order to _____ the contents so she could close it.

15. Her emotional _____ to the surprise party was something no one had anticipated.

3

C. Fill in the bubble next to the answer that best completes the sentence or answers the question.

16. A *luminous* object is
    - ○ **A** sparkly
    - ○ **B** slippery
    - ○ **C** famous
    - ○ **D** round

17. Read this sentence:
    A *compound* of crushed aspirin and water can relieve the itch of mosquito bites.

    Compound means
    - ○ **A** lotion
    - ○ **B** bandage
    - ○ **C** medicine
    - ○ **D** mixture

18. When your plans *coincide* with someone else's, they
    - ○ **A** interfere with each other
    - ○ **B** are in agreement
    - ○ **C** are repetitious
    - ○ **D** imitate each other

19. Another word for *overall* is
    - ○ **A** hopefully
    - ○ **B** completely
    - ○ **C** generally
    - ○ **D** possibly

20. When there is a *bond* between people, there is
    - ○ **A** a strong tie
    - ○ **B** an obligation
    - ○ **C** competition
    - ○ **D** unpleasantness

21. Read this sentence:
    Two-story houses *comprise* the buildings on my block.

    Comprise means
    - ○ **A** surround
    - ○ **B** fill out
    - ○ **C** make up
    - ○ **D** complete

22. What does a security guard *monitor* at a store?
    - ○ **A** shoppers' behavior
    - ○ **B** discount prices
    - ○ **C** employee schedules
    - ○ **D** the help desk

23. Which of these would cause *combustion*?
    - ○ **A** a broken water pipe
    - ○ **B** a dropped plate
    - ○ **C** a spark in dry leaves
    - ○ **D** a water balloon

24. A synonym for *compress* is
    - ○ **A** blend
    - ○ **B** complicate
    - ○ **C** inhibit
    - ○ **D** squeeze

25. The usual *reaction* to a joke is
    - ○ **A** silence
    - ○ **B** laughter
    - ○ **C** nods
    - ○ **D** comedy

4

Name _____ Date _____ Class _____

Is There Life on Mars?

| administration | constrained | investment | percentage | resources |
| celestial | immense | orbit | privilege | satellite |

A. From the Word Bank above, choose the word that best matches each meaning. Write the word on the line provided.

1. _____ Confined or limited

2. _____ A special right or advantage

3. _____ An object that moves in a circle around Earth or another planet

4. _____ To travel in a circle around another object

5. _____ The process of managing or supervising an activity

6. _____ Having to do with what is visible in the sky from Earth

7. _____ A part or fraction of the whole

8. _____ Huge in size or degree

9. _____ Things that make life or another undertaking possible

10. _____ Time or money devoted to something with the expectation of some benefit

B. Choose one of the words in the Word Bank above to complete each sentence. Write the word on the line provided.

11. The first space shuttle mission took place early in President Ronald Reagan's

_____.

12. The doctor works in a medical center that's a/an _____ of the hospital.

13. My _____ working as a volunteer at the library during the school year was a good idea, because I was offered a summer job.

14. Our favorite uncle promised to _____ us with a visit at Thanksgiving.

15. My family's vacation plans were _____ by a lack of money.

C. Fill in the bubble next to the answer that best completes the sentence or answers the question.

16. Which of these is the most *immense*?
    ○ **A** mouse
    ○ **B** human being
    ○ **C** bike
    ○ **D** car

17. Read this sentence:
    A meteor shower is a *celestial* light show.

    Celestial means
    ○ **A** in the sky
    ○ **B** brief
    ○ **C** religious
    ○ **D** delightful

18. Where would you be most likely to feel *constrained*?
    ○ **A** on a fast scooter
    ○ **B** in the cafeteria
    ○ **C** at a crowded event
    ○ **D** in an open field

19. A verb similar in meaning to *orbit* is
    ○ **A** flow
    ○ **B** progress
    ○ **C** repeat
    ○ **D** circle

20. Which of these requires financial *resources*?
    ○ **A** starting a new business
    ○ **B** working at an office
    ○ **C** attending public school
    ○ **D** being a cashier

21. Read this sentence:
    Xiomara considered it a *privilege* to be part of the reading circle.

    Privilege means
    ○ **A** honor
    ○ **B** obligation
    ○ **C** expectation
    ○ **D** right

22. A *percentage* of the students in our class walk to school.
    ○ **A** majority
    ○ **B** portion
    ○ **C** minority
    ○ **D** delegation

23. The person responsible for the *administration* of a new program will
    ○ **A** supervise it
    ○ **B** finance it
    ○ **C** evaluate it
    ○ **D** design it

24. When you make an *investment*, you
    ○ **A** donate money
    ○ **B** place a bet
    ○ **C** buy something expensive
    ○ **D** devote time or money

25. A corporation opened a *satellite* office. It set up the office
    ○ **A** to serve as the company headquarters
    ○ **B** to make the headquarters bigger
    ○ **C** to be a separate office from the headquarters
    ○ **D** to start a different company

6

Tania Léon Follows Her Music

displaced	founder	illusion	occupied	ration
enhance	harmony	moral	prominent	restrained

A. From the Word Bank above, choose the word that best matches each meaning. Write the word on the line provided.

1. _____ Having to do with right and wrong

2. _____ Forced to leave home

3. _____ A person who establishes something

4. _____ Having control over emotions

5. _____ Noticeable or well known

6. _____ To increase the quality of something or make it better

7. _____ An arrangement of parts that makes something pleasing or balanced and in agreement

8. _____ A mistaken impression or belief

9. _____ To limit or distribute something equally

10. _____ Resided or lived in as an owner or tenant

B. Choose one of the words in the Word Bank above to complete each sentence. Write the word on the line provided.

11. We watched the toy sailboat _____ and then sink in the pool.

12. The image of ourselves that we carry in our heads is often a/an _____ and very different from what others see.

13. Most of the piano students preferred to play familiar tunes, but Kara liked to play chords and listen to the _____ they created.

14. Our dog would eat two times his daily _____ of food if we let him.

15. I like to read fables and guess the _____ the story is trying to tell me.

C. Fill in the bubble next to the answer that best completes the sentence or answers the question.

16. People who are *displaced* have been
    ○ **A** offered different jobs
    ○ **B** moved from their regular homes
    ○ **C** voted into political office
    ○ **D** asked politely to leave

17. Read this sentence:
    They planted the rosebush in a *prominent* place in their garden.

    Prominent means
    ○ **A** noticeable
    ○ **B** hilly
    ○ **C** well cared for
    ○ **D** fenced

18. A person who is *restrained* would NOT
    ○ **A** say "Thank you"
    ○ **B** behave calmly
    ○ **C** act like a clown
    ○ **D** be polite

19. The opposite of *occupied* is
    ○ **A** empty
    ○ **B** uncommon
    ○ **C** quiet
    ○ **D** frequent

20. If ideas are in *harmony,* they are
    ○ **A** related to music
    ○ **B** in great contrast
    ○ **C** pleasing to everyone
    ○ **D** in agreement

21. Read this sentence:
    Tomas lives with the *illusion* that everyone's family is exactly like his.

    An *illusion* is a/an
    ○ **A** mental picture
    ○ **B** firm belief
    ○ **C** happy thought
    ○ **D** incorrect idea

22. If a story has a *moral,* it
    ○ **A** has characters who are good
    ○ **B** has a happy ending
    ○ **C** teaches a lesson
    ○ **D** has a conflict

23. The *founder* of a company
    ○ **A** created the company
    ○ **B** works for the company
    ○ **C** caused the company to fail
    ○ **D** is in competition with the company

24. You might *ration* your food if you
    ○ **A** had too much food
    ○ **B** didn't want others to eat it
    ○ **C** didn't want to eat too much
    ○ **D** were very hungry

25. What could *enhance* the appeal of a room?
    ○ **A** old curtains
    ○ **B** dirty carpeting
    ○ **C** colorful flowers
    ○ **D** a table and chairs

8

A Slave Remembers

agency	condemn	indication	periodical	trace
bondage	contradiction	isolation	radical	verdict

A. From the Word Bank above, choose the word that best matches each meaning. Write the word on the line provided.

1. _____ The state of being bound or enslaved

2. _____ Appearing from time to time

3. _____ Extreme or unusual

4. _____ To declare that something is wrong or unfit

5. _____ A decision made by a jury in court

6. _____ A mark left behind that shows that someone has been there

7. _____ A symptom or sign

8. _____ The state of being alone or separated from others

9. _____ The power by which something is done

10. _____ A statement or situation in which two things do not agree

B. Choose one of the words in the Word Bank above to complete each sentence. Write the word on the line provided.

11. In the waiting room, Omar flipped through the pages of a/an _____.

12. The Martins had a travel _____ make all of the arrangements for their trip to China.

13. Although I supported his cause, I did not agree when the _____ began breaking the law to gain attention for his point of view.

14. I told my parents why I thought I should be able to get a part-time job, and now I am waiting for their _____.

15. Dark clouds are often a/an _____ that it's going to rain.

C. Fill in the bubble next to the answer that best completes the sentence or answers the question.

16. People in *bondage* are
- ○ **A** employed
- ○ **B** bankers
- ○ **C** tenants
- ○ **D** enslaved

17. Read this sentence:

Everything he said yesterday was a *contradiction* of something he had said before.

A *contradiction* is a statement that
- ○ **A** supports an opinion
- ○ **B** repeats a point of view
- ○ **C** says the opposite
- ○ **D** disproves a fact

18. Which of these would be a *radical* approach to reducing energy consumption?
- ○ **A** creating bike paths
- ○ **B** banning all cars
- ○ **C** turning out lights earlier
- ○ **D** unplugging appliances

19. A word associated with *verdict* is
- ○ **A** truth
- ○ **B** announcement
- ○ **C** judgment
- ○ **D** evaluation

20. If you *trace* a pattern, you
- ○ **A** copy it
- ○ **B** draw it
- ○ **C** cut it out
- ○ **D** design it

21. Read this sentence:

The children showed no *indication* that they were listening, yet they heard everything that was said.

Indication means
- ○ **A** reaction
- ○ **B** habit
- ○ **C** preference
- ○ **D** sign

22. Which is a *periodical* event?
- ○ **A** one that ought to happen
- ○ **B** one that never happens
- ○ **C** one that happens weekly
- ○ **D** one that might happen one day

23. If someone likes to work in *isolation*, she prefers to work
- ○ **A** in a cold room
- ○ **B** in an empty room
- ○ **C** away from other people
- ○ **D** in absolute quiet

24. A government *agency*
- ○ **A** is part of the government
- ○ **B** is separate from the government
- ○ **C** controls the government
- ○ **D** is bigger than the government

25. If you *condemn* an action, you
- ○ **A** keep it from happening
- ○ **B** try to undo it
- ○ **C** make a public apology
- ○ **D** say it was wrong

10

Name _____ Date _____ Class _____

Following Lewis and Clark

discrimination	expedition	mishap	perspective	route
episode	log	overtake	recover	visible

A. From the Word Bank above, choose the word that best matches each meaning. Write the word on the line provided.

1. _____ A path or course taken for travel

2. _____ The practice of treating a person or group of people unfairly

3. _____ A noteworthy or meaningful event

4. _____ To record information

5. _____ An unfortunate accident

6. _____ Able to be seen

7. _____ To come over something suddenly

8. _____ To return to normal

9. _____ The view of things from a certain vantage point

10. _____ A journey taken for a specific purpose

B. Choose one of the words in the Word Bank above to complete each sentence. Write the word on the line provided.

11. From Shandra's _____ on top of the Ferris wheel, everyone on the ground looked no bigger than mice.

12. I try not to miss each new _____ of my favorite podcast.

13. Trey hoped to _____ his lost luggage before returning home from his vacation.

14. When the bicyclists saw the roadblock ahead, they knew they would have to find a new _____ home.

15. The spider web is so tiny and delicate, it is barely _____.

C. Fill in the bubble next to the answer that best completes the sentence or answers the question.

16. When you plan your *route,* you decide
○ **A** where you might go
○ **B** what roads you will take
○ **C** when you will leave and arrive
○ **D** your reason for going

17. Read this sentence:

Admiral William Parry led the earliest *expedition* to the North Pole in 1827.

An *expedition* is a

○ **A** journey for a specific purpose
○ **B** vacation in distant places
○ **C** trip taken on a dare
○ **D** journey that involves different types of transportation

18. When misfortunes *overtake* you, they
○ **A** pass you by
○ **B** are part of your life
○ **C** come over you suddenly
○ **D** can be ignored

19. The opposite of *visible* is
○ **A** accessible
○ **B** sightless
○ **C** obvious
○ **D** hidden

20. What would NOT be a *mishap*?
○ **A** slipping on a banana peel
○ **B** getting into a dented car
○ **C** running into a hole
○ **D** falling into a puddle

21. Read this sentence:

The police were able to *recover* the stolen items and return them to their owners.

Recover means

○ **A** replace
○ **B** investigate
○ **C** get back
○ **D** locate

22. When you *log* information, you
○ **A** record it
○ **B** memorize it
○ **C** erase it
○ **D** publish it

23. If you have a different *perspective* on something, you have
○ **A** a better opinion of it
○ **B** a different view of it
○ **C** a clearer understanding
○ **D** no opinion about it

24. If you shop with *discrimination,* you
○ **A** prefer to shop online
○ **B** shop only with people your own age
○ **C** refuse to go to shopping malls
○ **D** make careful choices

25. An *episode* of a TV series is
○ **A** one season
○ **B** the plot
○ **C** one show
○ **D** a favorite part

12

Do Cereals Really Contain Iron?

clarify	domain	intensify	precede	signify
diversity	element	phenomenon	representation	tangible

A. From the Word Bank above, choose the word that best matches each meaning. Write the word on the line provided.

1. _____ To make stronger

2. _____ To come before

3. _____ To explain or make something easier to understand

4. _____ To increase the variety

5. _____ A part of a whole or an ingredient

6. _____ To be a sign of or to show

7. _____ An area of knowledge or study

8. _____ Able to be touched or understood

9. _____ The way something is portrayed

10. _____ An event known through the senses

B. Choose one of the words in the Word Bank above to complete each sentence. Write the word on the line provided.

11. Every state has equal _____ in the United States Senate.

12. The grocery store owner knew the shoppers didn't like to eat the same kind of fruit all the time, so he decided to _____ his produce.

13. The tyrant hoped to increase his _____ by taking over the country next to his.

14. The speaker was happy to _____ any points the audience didn't understand.

15. At a wedding, the bridesmaids _____ the bride down the aisle.

C. Fill in the bubble next to the answer that best completes the sentence or answers the question.

16. If you *intensify* the flavor of what you're cooking, you
   - ○ **A** strengthen it
   - ○ **B** weaken it
   - ○ **C** test it
   - ○ **D** sweeten it

17. Read this sentence:

    The novel provides an accurate *representation* of life in London in the 1870s.

    Representation means
   - ○ **A** description
   - ○ **B** fiction
   - ○ **C** history
   - ○ **D** memory

18. If you *precede* someone through a doorway, you
   - ○ **A** wait your turn
   - ○ **B** hold the door
   - ○ **C** open the door
   - ○ **D** go first

19. A synonym of *tangible* is
   - ○ **A** manageable
   - ○ **B** imagined
   - ○ **C** touchable
   - ○ **D** agreeable

20. The nail factory decided to *diversify* in order to
   - ○ **A** increase the cost of nails
   - ○ **B** stop making nails
   - ○ **C** make more nails
   - ○ **D** make something besides nails

21. Read this sentence:

    Dad checks with Mom before making plans, because managing the family calendar is her *domain*.

    Domain means
   - ○ **A** main occupation
   - ○ **B** area of knowledge
   - ○ **C** difficult subject
   - ○ **D** location

22. Which of the following statements is NOT true of a *phenomenon*?
   - ○ **A** It can be explained by science.
   - ○ **B** It is experienced by the senses.
   - ○ **C** It happens only in your mind.
   - ○ **D** It can be observed.

23. Which of these is an *element* of pizza?
   - ○ **A** an oven
   - ○ **B** the pan
   - ○ **C** the crust
   - ○ **D** a party

24. Another word for *signify* is
   - ○ **A** display
   - ○ **B** show
   - ○ **C** exhibit
   - ○ **D** flaunt

25. You would ask someone to *clarify* something if you
   - ○ **A** didn't understand it
   - ○ **B** couldn't see it
   - ○ **C** hadn't heard it
   - ○ **D** wanted proof it was true

14

Name _____ Date _____ Class _____

Two-Time Nobel Prize Winner Dies

advocate	civilian	interval	particles	succession
civil	innovation	nuclear	radioactive	welfare

A. From the Word Bank above, choose the word that best matches each meaning. Write the word on the line provided.

1. _____ Giving off atomic energy when broken down

2. _____ Polite, well-mannered, and courteous

3. _____ A new product, idea, or way to do something

4. _____ A number of things that follow each other in order

5. _____ Relating to power sources that use energy from atoms

6. _____ Relating to people not in the military

7. _____ Tiny parts or pieces

8. _____ A person who speaks out for another person

9. _____ A state of happiness, good fortune, well-being, and health

10. _____ The amount of time between two events

B. Choose one of the words in the Word Bank above to complete each sentence. Write the word on the line provided.

11. Prince Charles is first in the line of _____ to the British throne.

12. People often do not understand the importance of _____ rights until they learn about life in places where those rights do not exist.

13. The _____ between the time when the clock tower strikes 12 noon and when it strikes 1 p.m. is exactly one hour.

14. Some politicians say that _____ power is this country's best alternative to coal and other traditional energy sources.

15. Kent used a dust cloth to remove the _____ from the computer screen.

C. Fill in the bubble next to the answer that best completes the sentence or answers the question.

16. If you *advocate* for an idea, you
    ○ **A** prove it to be true
    ○ **B** criticize it
    ○ **C** oppose it
    ○ **D** support it

17. Read this sentence:
    Parents are concerned for the *welfare* of their children.

    Welfare means
    ○ **A** health and well-being
    ○ **B** financial assistance
    ○ **C** diet and nutrition
    ○ **D** education expenses

18. If someone speaks in a *civil* manner, she
    ○ **A** speaks for everyone's benefit
    ○ **B** talks like a regular person
    ○ **C** speaks in a respectful way
    ○ **D** communicates with neighbors

19. Another word for *interval* is
    ○ **A** sequence
    ○ **B** gap
    ○ **C** barrier
    ○ **D** continuation

20. Which of the following groups is part of the *civilian* community?
    ○ **A** police officers
    ○ **B** soldiers
    ○ **C** schoolchildren
    ○ **D** firefighters

21. Read this sentence:
    After a *succession* of solid wins, the team suffered a disappointing loss to its greatest rival.

    Succession means
    ○ **A** things that are successful
    ○ **B** group of three
    ○ **C** things that follow each other
    ○ **D** tournament games

22. *Nuclear* reactions create
    ○ **A** energy
    ○ **B** food
    ○ **C** sunshine
    ○ **D** families

23. *Particles* are
    ○ **A** dividers
    ○ **B** parts of speech
    ○ **C** fractions
    ○ **D** tiny pieces

24. If you introduce an *innovation,* you
    ○ **A** repair something that is old
    ○ **B** create something entirely new
    ○ **C** suggest a change of plan
    ○ **D** present an inventor

25. Something that is *radioactive*
    ○ **A** transmits radio signals
    ○ **B** receives radio signals
    ○ **C** gives off atomic energy
    ○ **D** is busy communicating with anothers

16

The Tennessee Coal Ash Case

differentiate	professional	properties	remedy	status
endeavor	prohibit	protocols	sinister	tolerate

A. From the Word Bank above, choose the word that best matches each meaning. Write the word on the line provided.

1. _____ Land and buildings

2. _____ To detect a difference between things

3. _____ To work with the purpose of accomplishing a task

4. _____ Evil or causing fear

5. _____ To put up with or allow something to continue

6. _____ Related to a job that requires specific knowledge or education

7. _____ To correct, cure, or make better

8. _____ To use authority to forbid something

9. _____ Rules that establish the correct way to behave

10. _____ A legal state or condition

B. Choose one of the words in the Word Bank above to complete each sentence. Write the word on the line provided.

11. The music turned _____ when the villain came on the screen.

12. If you want to get good medical advice, it's best to talk to a/an _____ who has the proper training.

13. Transforming the front yard into a vegetable garden was a/an _____ that involved the whole family and a few helpful neighbors.

14. A shiny appearance is one of the _____ shared by most metals.

15. Although there is no cure for the common cold, everyone has a favorite _____ for treating its symptoms.

C. Fill in the bubble next to the answer that best completes the sentence or answers the question.

16. When you *remedy* a disease, you do NOT
- ○ **A** worsen it
- ○ **B** cure it
- ○ **C** improve it
- ○ **D** correct it

17. Read this sentence:

My parents always hire a *professional* accountant to complete their tax return.

A *professional* is
- ○ **A** someone who knows math well
- ○ **B** someone with special knowledge
- ○ **C** someone with a lot of experience
- ○ **D** someone at a government office

18. If you can *tolerate* pain, you
- ○ **A** take pain medication
- ○ **B** can't feel it
- ○ **C** can deal with it
- ○ **D** feel it only sometimes

19. A word closely related to *endeavor* is
- ○ **A** failure
- ○ **B** success
- ○ **C** struggle
- ○ **D** activity

20. If you ask about the *protocols* of visiting the White House, you want to know
- ○ **A** the visiting hours
- ○ **B** the public entrances
- ○ **C** the rules for behavior
- ○ **D** the officials you might meet

21. Read this sentence:

In order to get a U.S. passport, you must have the *status* of a citizen.

Status means
- ○ **A** residence
- ○ **B** popularity
- ○ **C** legal condition
- ○ **D** document

22. A *sinister* look might cause
- ○ **A** fear
- ○ **B** confidence
- ○ **C** self-doubt
- ○ **D** creativity

23. If mustard and ketchup have similar *properties,* they
- ○ **A** taste almost the same
- ○ **B** have many of the same ingredients
- ○ **C** share some qualities
- ○ **D** have similar uses

24. The best synonym for *prohibit* is
- ○ **A** encourage
- ○ **B** forbid
- ○ **C** block
- ○ **D** delay

25. If you're able to *differentiate* between the things you need and the things you want, you can
- ○ **A** explain what they have in common
- ○ **B** always get what you want
- ○ **C** see the common characteristics
- ○ **D** recognize the difference

Coming to Ellis Island

apparel	eliminate	intrinsically	positive	secure
duration	feeble	negative	rejected	stifle

A. From the Word Bank above, choose the word that best matches each meaning. Write the word on the line provided.

1. _____ Very weak or lacking strength

2. _____ Confident, safe, and free from danger

3. _____ Optimistic and having a good effect

4. _____ To get rid of or put an end to

5. _____ Article of clothing

6. _____ Unfavorable or disagreeable

7. _____ Not accepted or sent away

8. _____ In a manner related to the basic nature of a being or object

9. _____ To try to prevent something from happening

10. _____ The period during which something happens or exists

B. Choose one of the words in the Word Bank above to complete each sentence. Write the word on the line provided.

11. My sister was _____ by three of the colleges she applied to, but she didn't mind since she was accepted by her first choice.

12. Since my mother was _____ she had put the permission slip in my backpack, she made me search through it again.

13. Jaime hopes to _____ a job at a local hospital as a nurse.

14. The only _____ about our new neighborhood is there is no dog park, so we have to walk around the block several times to give our beagle exercise.

15. It's hard for someone who is _____ open and honest to keep a secret.

C. Fill in the bubble next to the answer that best completes the sentence or answers the question.

16. When you feel *secure,* you feel
- ○ **A** trapped
- ○ **B** bored
- ○ **C** unable to move
- ○ **D** safe

17. Read this sentence:

Monica's gloomy attitude has a *negati* effect on everyone around h

Negative mea

- ○ **A** unfavorab
- ○ **B** motivating
- ○ **C** contrary
- ○ **D** reverse

18. If you sit through the ⌐tion of the performance, you are th for
- ○ **A** the last hour
- ○ **B** the entire thing
- ○ **C** the intermission
- ○ **D** the second half

19. The opposite of *feeble* is
- ○ **A** weak
- ○ **B** useless
- ○ **C** gentle
- ○ **D** strong

20. If someone possesses a quality *intrinsically,* it is
- ○ **A** something they learned
- ○ **B** part of their character
- ○ **C** a negative quality
- ○ **D** shared by the entire family

21. Read this sentence:

The struggling author was upset because nine publishers had *rejected* her manuscript.

Rejected means
- ○ **A** not returned
- ○ **B** criticized
- ○ **C** destroyed
- ○ **D** not accepted

22. If you are *positive* that it won't rain, you are
- ○ **A** happy it won't rain
- ○ **B** certain it won't rain
- ○ **C** hoping it won't rain
- ○ **D** afraid it will rain

23. Which set of things would you find in a store that sells only *apparel*?
- ○ **A** kayaks, bikes, skis
- ○ **B** books, uniforms, electronics
- ○ **C** jeans, shirts, sweaters
- ○ **D** calendars, T-shirts, greeting cards

24. A word closely related to *eliminate* is
- ○ **A** accept
- ○ **B** unwelcome
- ○ **C** disregard
- ○ **D** stop

25. When you *stifle* a grin, you try to
- ○ **A** keep from doing it
- ○ **B** do it without people noticing
- ○ **C** draw attention to yourself
- ○ **D** let people know that you're happy

20

Angel Island: A Letter Home

attainable	crisis	exploit	insightful	progress
conclude	exclusionary	include	preclude	stereotype

A. From the Word Bank above, choose the word that best matches each meaning. Write the word on the line provided.

1. _____ Able to understand situations clearly

2. _____ To make judgments about individuals based on general opinions of a whole group

3. _____ To use people to your own advantage

4. _____ Forward movement

5. _____ To make something impossible

6. _____ To make a decision using reasoning

7. _____ A changing situation that is likely to have a bad outcome

8. _____ Preventing certain people from participating

9. _____ To make a part of something bigger

10. _____ Able to be reached or achieved

B. Choose one of the words in the Word Bank above to complete each sentence. Write the word on the line provided.

11. Antonio finished his outline and will _____ to writing his essay.

12. Their busy schedules _____ their taking time off to play soccer.

13. A/An _____ of the elderly is that they are forgetful, but my grandmother has a better memory than I do.

14. The judge determined that the club's _____ policies were illegal, and that they had to allow any town resident to join.

15. The movie will _____ with the words "The End" and the closing credits.

C. Fill in the bubble next to the answer that best completes the sentence or answers the question.

16. A situation is a *crisis* when
   ○ **A** things are about to change
   ○ **B** a bad outcome seems possible
   ○ **C** nothing seems likely to change
   ○ **D** it ends well

17. Read the sentence:
   The *stereotype* that young children care only about themselves is unfair.

   A *stereotype* is
   ○ **A** a mental image of a group
   ○ **B** someone who speaks for a group
   ○ **C** a written description
   ○ **D** a first impression

18. Policies that are *exclusionary* do NOT
   ○ **A** leave people out
   ○ **B** consider people differently
   ○ **C** include everyone
   ○ **D** include only certain groups

19. When you *exploit* a situation, you
   ○ **A** take advantage of it
   ○ **B** consider others' needs
   ○ **C** take action without thinking
   ○ **D** experience a setback

20. When circumstances *preclude* having a pet, they
   ○ **A** encourage pet adoption
   ○ **B** provide basic information about pet ownership
   ○ **C** provide a suitable home for a pet
   ○ **D** rule out the idea of having a pet

21. Read this sentence:
   The school orchestra will *conclude* the concert with a performance of "We Are the World."

   In this sentence, *conclude* means
   ○ **A** begin
   ○ **B** end
   ○ **C** celebrate
   ○ **D** repeat

22. When *progress* is made, things
   ○ **A** are delayed
   ○ **B** advance too quickly
   ○ **C** move forward
   ○ **D** become disorganized

23. When you *include* a friend in your plans, you
   ○ **A** tell him what you'll do alone
   ○ **B** send him notes and post cards
   ○ **C** try to avoid him
   ○ **D** make him part of the plans

24. An *attainable* goal is one you
   ○ **A** set for yourself
   ○ **B** can achieve
   ○ **C** reach on your own
   ○ **D** have been assigned

25. Another person's *insightful* comments can help you
   ○ **A** express yourself better
   ○ **B** win an argument
   ○ **C** see things more clearly
   ○ **D** get more confused

Who Was Here First?

calamity	convert	logically	onslaught	subsequently
conform	intelligence	margins	plea	uniquely

A. From the Word Bank above, choose the word that best matches each meaning. Write the word on the line provided.

1. _____ Coming afterward

2. _____ In an orderly way that follows reason

3. _____ To change from one form or system to another

4. _____ An attack or something that feels like an attack

5. _____ A disastrous event that causes loss, trouble, or suffering

6. _____ The extra amounts that allow for special situations without causing difficulties or concern

7. _____ To follow the established order

8. _____ The ability to use knowledge in new situations

9. _____ Unusually or in a way that is without equal

10. _____ An urgent request

B. Choose one of the words in the Word Bank above to complete each sentence. Write the word on the line provided.

11. When Peyton served Terri a new kind of ice cream, Terri became a/an _____ and switched brands.

12. The man accused of stealing a car entered a/an _____ of "not guilty."

13. Although my father waded into the lake to fish, my sister and I cast our fishing lines from the _____.

14. Spies gather _____ about an enemy's plans and movements.

15. The house suffered serious damage in a fire and was _____ torn down.

C. Fill in the bubble next to the answer that best completes the sentence or answers the question.

16. If someone is *uniquely* talented, no one else
    ○ **A** is likely to notice
    ○ **B** possesses the same skills
    ○ **C** appreciates his abilities
    ○ **D** can compete with him

17. Read this sentence:
    When the power goes out, the electric company must deal with an *onslaught* of phone calls.

    Onslaught means
    ○ **A** the beginning
    ○ **B** complaints
    ○ **C** angry
    ○ **D** a lot of

18. When people's ideas *conform* with the group's beliefs, they do NOT
    ○ **A** disagree with the group
    ○ **B** fit in
    ○ **C** wish to be a member
    ○ **D** support the group

19. A word closely associated with *convert* is
    ○ **A** substitute
    ○ **B** remain
    ○ **C** influence
    ○ **D** transform

20. If you stand on the *margins* of the crowd, you are
    ○ **A** in the middle of the group
    ○ **B** above the group
    ○ **C** right outside of the group
    ○ **D** nowhere near the group

21. Read this sentence:
    A flood is a *calamity* when people lose their homes.

    Calamity means
    ○ **A** disastrous event
    ○ **B** unexpected event
    ○ **C** historic occasion
    ○ **D** remarkable circumstance

22. If you make a *plea* for more time to finish a project, you make
    ○ **A** a persuasive argument
    ○ **B** a casual remark
    ○ **C** an urgent request
    ○ **D** a helpful suggestion

23. If something happens *subsequently*, it happens
    ○ **A** as the first event in a series
    ○ **B** over and over
    ○ **C** as a result of something
    ○ **D** after something else

24. When someone argues *logically,* she presents her ideas
    ○ **A** with a strong point of view
    ○ **B** in a well-reasoned manner
    ○ **C** with few examples
    ○ **D** in order of importance

25. A measure of *intelligence* is someone's ability to
    ○ **A** have an opinion on everything
    ○ **B** talk at length on any subject
    ○ **C** earn lots of money
    ○ **D** learn and use knowledge

24

Name _____ Date _____ Class _____

Mid-Year Test

combustion	convert	domain	onslaught	succession
compress	differentiate	element	precede	suspend
condemn	discrimination	harmony	resolve	tolerate

A. From the Word Bank above, choose the word that best matches each meaning. Write the word on the line provided.

1. _____ To make a firm decision to do something

2. _____ An area of study or knowledge

3. _____ A part of the whole of something

4. _____ To put up with or allow to continue

5. _____ Ability to see fine differences in things and judge what's best

6. _____ To change to a different form or system

7. _____ To declare something to be wrong or evil

8. _____ To press or squeeze together

9. _____ A balanced or pleasing arrangement

10. _____ To stop temporarily

B. Choose one of the words in the Word Bank above to complete each sentence. Write the word on the line provided.

11. A computer spell check might not _____ between *its* and *it's*.

12. When Miss Applegate was out sick for four months, we had a/an _____ of substitute teachers who each lasted a few weeks.

13. Despite the scandal, he ignored the reporters' _____ of questions.

14. Firefighters warn that dry weather and high temperatures encourage _____.

15. Did John Adams _____ Thomas Jefferson as President, or did he come after Jefferson?

C. Fill in the bubble next to the answer that best completes the sentence or answers the question.

16. Which person is *displaced*?
    ○ **A** Gilles has moved to a new apartment in a nearby city.
    ○ **B** Ana lives temporarily with an aunt because her house burned down.
    ○ **C** Davonn lives in a college dormitory.
    ○ **D** Noam is visiting relatives in Mexico.

17. Which of the following would you call an *expedition*?
    ○ **A** a ride to school on a school bus
    ○ **B** a journey down the Amazon River
    ○ **C** a trip to the supermarket
    ○ **D** a four-hour visit to the library

18. The Milky Way, our *galaxy*, is made up of
    ○ **A** countless stars and planets
    ○ **B** Earth and its moon
    ○ **C** a few well-known constellations
    ○ **D** the sun, the moon, and Earth

19. Read this sentence:

    After more than a year, Bobbie called and made a *feeble* attempt to apologize.

    Feeble means
    ○ **A** late
    ○ **B** awkward
    ○ **C** sincere
    ○ **D** weak

20. A ship is most likely to *founder* when it
    ○ **A** is safely docked in port
    ○ **B** is being built in a shipyard
    ○ **C** runs into a huge iceberg
    ○ **D** sails in a stormy sea

21. An argument that is *logically* organized
    ○ **A** is impossible to understand
    ○ **B** is reasonable and makes sense
    ○ **C** states someone's opinion
    ○ **D** lacks reasons and evidence

22. How might you *exploit* a power failure?
    ○ **A** Use it as an excuse for not doing your homework.
    ○ **B** Find out why it happened.
    ○ **C** Offer to help your neighbors.
    ○ **D** Be prepared with flashlights and extra batteries.

23. Which circumstance might *preclude* your getting to school on time?
    ○ **A** You have an important test today.
    ○ **B** You forgot to eat breakfast.
    ○ **C** Twelve inches of snow fell during he night.
    ○ **D** Today is your birthday.

24. Read this sentence:

    Jack's mom keeps telling him that "Hey you!" is not a *civil* greeting.

    Civil means
    ○ **A** polite
    ○ **B** adult
    ○ **C** cheerful
    ○ **D** helpful

25. An *insightful* person is likely to
    ○ **A** make bad decisions without looking ahead
    ○ **B** jump to the wrong conclusion
    ○ **C** act right away, without thinking
    ○ **D** have a clear understanding of people and situations

Name _____ Date _____ Class _____

The Great Climb

descend	endure	frigid	pinnacle	survey
elevate	force	gravity	ramble	unaffected

A. From the Word Bank above, choose the word that best matches each meaning. Write the word on the line provided.

1. _____ The highest point

2. _____ To move from a higher place to a lower place

3. _____ The power or energy applied to something

4. _____ To suffer through a hardship

5. _____ Not changed in any way

6. _____ An aimless walk that a person takes for pleasure

7. _____ Extremely cold

8. _____ To raise or lift something higher

9. _____ A general inspection of the situation

10. _____ The attraction between Earth and objects

B. Choose one of the words in the Word Bank above to complete each sentence. Write the word on the line provided.

11. My mother told me not to _____ home from school because I needed to get to my doctor's appointment on time.

12. If you try to _____ the suitcase closed, you will break the latch.

13. Before entering, Chris stopped to _____ the room.

14. At first, Danilo seemed _____ and unfriendly, but once Indira got to know him, she could see that he was actually very warm and kind.

15. Everyone was quiet and respectful, because they sensed the _____ of the situation.

27

C. Fill in the bubble next to the answer that best completes the sentence or answers the question.

16. In which sport do you succeed by overcoming *gravity*?
    ○ **A** soccer
    ○ **B** cycling
    ○ **C** wrestling
    ○ **D** high jump

17. Read this sentence:
    The South Pole is one of the most *frigid* places on Earth.

    Frigid means
    ○ **A** distant
    ○ **B** very cold
    ○ **C** difficult
    ○ **D** barren

18. When you *ramble,* you
    ○ **A** take the most direct path
    ○ **B** walk with no real plan
    ○ **C** run in the opposite direction
    ○ **D** stumble over something

19. A synonym for *elevate* is
    ○ **A** lift
    ○ **B** decorate
    ○ **C** climb
    ○ **D** diminish

20. If someone is at the *pinnacle* of her career, she is
    ○ **A** just starting out
    ○ **B** ready to retire
    ○ **C** at the highest point
    ○ **D** in a difficult phase

21. Read this sentence:
    Carla made a *survey* of the books on her bookshelf to see which one she wanted to read next.

    Survey means
    ○ **A** complete list
    ○ **B** general look
    ○ **C** small sampling
    ○ **D** summary

22. Which of the following would someone have to *endure*?
    ○ **A** good news
    ○ **B** happiness
    ○ **C** sleep
    ○ **D** problems

23. Which of these does a person *descend*?
    ○ **A** a table
    ○ **B** an elevator
    ○ **C** a pen
    ○ **D** a staircase

24. A synonym for *force* is
    ○ **A** persuade
    ○ **B** convince
    ○ **C** require
    ○ **D** decide

25. People who are *unaffected* by wealth and privilege are
    ○ **A** ungrateful
    ○ **B** poor and helpless
    ○ **C** genuine and natural
    ○ **D** unimpressed

28

Surfing the Big Waves

appreciate	deviate	fatigue	momentum	prioritize
contemporary	disproportionately	induce	persist	swell

A. From the Word Bank above, choose the word that best matches each meaning. Write the word on the line provided.

1. _____ To change or move from a planned path or plan

2. _____ To put things in order of importance

3. _____ The feeling of being tired from hard work

4. _____ To continue even when you are warned not to

5. _____ To expand in size, volume, or number

6. _____ To cause something to happen

7. _____ Displaying a major difference in size or another characteristic

8. _____ To understand the quality, value, or significance of something

9. _____ Modern or current

10. _____ The force that causes an object in motion to keep moving

B. Choose one of the words in the Word Bank above to complete each sentence. Write the word on the line provided.

11. People hope their houses will _____ in value over time, so they will be worth more when they sell them than when they bought them.

12. Stress and mental strain can _____ you as much as physical exercise.

13. As long as you don't _____ from the directions, you'll make it to the movie on time.

14. Maggie's teacher is a/an _____ of her parents and attended high school with them.

15. _____ keeps a wagon rolling downhill.

C. Fill in the bubble next to the answer that best completes the sentence or answers the question.

16. A word closely associated with *swell* is
    - ○ **A** blast
    - ○ **B** wave
    - ○ **C** pleasure
    - ○ **D** boastful

17. Read this sentence:

    When you have lots of work to do, it's important to *prioritize* the tasks.

    Prioritize means
    - ○ **A** arrange in order of importance
    - ○ **B** work before doing other things
    - ○ **C** do nothing but your work
    - ○ **D** work until the last task is finished

18. Which two things compare *disproportionately* in size with each other?
    - ○ **A** a lion and a tiger
    - ○ **B** an oak tree and an elm tree
    - ○ **C** a dump truck and a tricycle
    - ○ **D** an apple and an orange

19. A word closely associated with *contemporary* is
    - ○ **A** futuristic
    - ○ **B** current
    - ○ **C** classical
    - ○ **D** fashionable

20. When paintings *appreciate*, they
    - ○ **A** appeal to art collectors
    - ○ **B** are liked by a variety of people
    - ○ **C** are shown in art galleries
    - ○ **D** increase in value

21. Read this sentence:

    They sat in the shade sipping lemonade, and nothing could *induce* them to leave that spot.

    In this sentence, *induce* means
    - ○ **A** convince
    - ○ **B** attract
    - ○ **C** upset
    - ○ **D** comfort

22. Which of the following does NOT develop *momentum*?
    - ○ **A** a skateboard on a ramp
    - ○ **B** a rolling stone on a slope
    - ○ **C** a statue on a platform
    - ○ **D** a sports car descending a hill

23. Which of these is the usual cause of *fatigue*?
    - ○ **A** getting a disappointing grade
    - ○ **B** thinking about pleasant things
    - ○ **C** eating too many sweets
    - ○ **D** working long and hard

24. What is the opposite of *persist*?
    - ○ **A** finish
    - ○ **B** give up
    - ○ **C** tolerate
    - ○ **D** carry on

25. If you have to *deviate* from your original plan, you probably
    - ○ **A** were having trouble
    - ○ **B** thought things were going well
    - ○ **C** never changed your mind
    - ○ **D** are very stubborn

30

The Magic of Paragliding

| abandon | accelerate | adjust | hover | speed |
| abstract | adaptable | dismay | rate | terminate |

A. From the Word Bank above, choose the word that best matches each meaning. Write the word on the line provided.

1. _____ The rate at which something happens or an object moves

2. _____ To leave an item or to withdraw from an activity

3. _____ To bring something to an end

4. _____ A measurement that compares two things

5. _____ To remain suspended in the air over one place

6. _____ To bring something to a more satisfactory state or place

7. _____ Existing only in the mind

8. _____ Able to be made to fit or be used for different situations

9. _____ Sudden surprising disappointment

10. _____ To make something go faster

B. Choose one of the words in the Word Bank above to complete each sentence. Write the word on the line provided.

11. It is never wise to _____ when driving, since you might crash if you go beyond the legal limits.

12. The fans cheered and waved their arms with wild _____ when their team finally scored a goal.

13. The librarian said she would _____ my computer session after thirty minutes so someone else could have a turn.

14. I read just the _____ since there was no time to read the whole article.

15. _____ the brightness of your monitor so the screen is easier to read.

C. Fill in the bubble next to the answer that best completes the sentence or answers the question.

16. When you feel *dismay,* you are
- ○ **A** frightened
- ○ **B** angry
- ○ **C** desperate
- ○ **D** disappointed

17. Read this sentence:

Hummingbirds *hover* as they drink the nectar from flowers.

Hover means
- ○ **A** hang in the air
- ○ **B** dart back and forth
- ○ **C** fly at great speed
- ○ **D** float on air currents

18. When children *abandon* a new toy, they
- ○ **A** put it on the shelf
- ○ **B** break it and get upset
- ○ **C** stop playing with it
- ○ **D** give it to someone

19. When you *adjust* the seat in a car, you
- ○ **A** fasten your seat belt
- ○ **B** decide where to sit
- ○ **C** move it to make it more comfortable
- ○ **D** change the upholstery

20. Which basic need is considered *abstract*?
- ○ **A** love
- ○ **B** food
- ○ **C** housing
- ○ **D** warmth

21. Read this sentence:

Dashiell decided to *terminate* his magazine subscription.

Terminate means
- ○ **A** renew
- ○ **B** end
- ○ **C** share
- ○ **D** buy

22. You would have to *accelerate* the schedule on a project to
- ○ **A** involve more people
- ○ **B** explain how it was done
- ○ **C** get it done faster
- ○ **D** show that you're organized

23. Cars that *speed* on a highway
- ○ **A** stop suddenly
- ○ **B** slow when there is another car
- ○ **C** enter the highway
- ○ **D** go faster than they should

24. A tool that is *adaptable*
- ○ **A** breaks easily
- ○ **B** has more than one purpose
- ○ **C** doesn't have a clear purpose
- ○ **D** runs on electricity

25. When you *rate* a movie, you
- ○ **A** decide if you want to see it
- ○ **B** recommend it to your friends
- ○ **C** make it one of your favorites
- ○ **D** compare it to others

32

The Rights for All

assemble	campaign	comprehensive	equity	mediate
behalf	capital	enforce	fragility	mutual

A. From the Word Bank above, choose the word that best matches each meaning. Write the word on the line provided.

1. _____ Actions taken to meet a goal or to get a certain result

2. _____ To make sure something gets done

3. _____ Shared by two or more people

4. _____ Easily broken, destroyed, or harmed

5. _____ Fairness and freedom from favoritism

6. _____ The worth of a person or organization

7. _____ To work to bring two people or groups together in order to find a solution to a problem

8. _____ To come together

9. _____ For another person's interest or benefit

10. _____ Including a broad range of information on a topic

B. Choose one of the words in the Word Bank above to complete each sentence. Write the word on the line provided.

11. It took us four hours to _____ the toy because it had so many parts.

12. The _____ on a home is its value above what is still owed on the loan.

13. Many people think the _____ of the state of New York is New York City, but it's actually Albany.

14. When my town announced it would tear down the historic library to build a parking garage, my brother began a/an _____ to protect the building.

15. Risa and Roberto go to different schools, but they have _____ friends.

C. Fill in the bubble next to the answer that best completes the sentence or answers the question.

16. Which item might you have to *assemble*?
- **A** a donut
- **B** a sandwich
- **C** a tree
- **D** water

17. Read this sentence:

Jody decided to undertake a *comprehensive* study of her favorite author.

Comprehensive means
- **A** voluntary
- **B** independent
- **C** well-defined
- **D** complete

18. Something that has *fragility* is
- **A** precise
- **B** flexible
- **C** tough
- **D** delicate

19. When you *enforce* the rules, you
- **A** make people follow them
- **B** make them stricter
- **C** protest against them
- **D** try to ignore them

20. *Capital* describes the
- **A** value of a company
- **B** location of a company
- **C** employees of a company
- **D** administration of a company

21. Read this sentence:

The candidate ran a positive *campaign* and said nothing bad about his opponent.

Campaign means
- **A** advertisement
- **B** effort to win an election
- **C** going door to door
- **D** making speeches

22. If you act on someone's *behalf,* you
- **A** complicate the person's plans
- **B** pretend to be that person
- **C** work for the person's benefit
- **D** are a relative of that person

23. A word closely associated with e*quity* is
- **A** share
- **B** value
- **C** ownership
- **D** equality

24. When you *mediate,* you try to
- **A** help opponents reach an agreement
- **B** clear your mind and relax
- **C** represent one side in a dispute
- **D** move to the center

25. I told Suzanne she was my best friend. When she said, "The feeling is *mutual,*" she meant
- **A** everyone felt the same way
- **B** I was her best friend, too
- **C** I was not her best friend
- **D** she was not sure how she felt

34

Name _____ Date _____ Class _____

Protecting the Wolf

captivity	conservation	incapacitated	qualitatively	tranquil
captured	engage	petition	savage	vegetate

A. From the Word Bank above, choose the word that best matches each meaning. Write the word on the line provided.

1. _____ To withdraw from physical or mental activity

2. _____ Calm, free from excitement, and undisturbed

3. _____ To take part in

4. _____ Untamed and wild

5. _____ To make a request for something you want or need

6. _____ Taken and kept

7. _____ The work of protecting something

8. _____ Comparing by characteristics, not number or amount

9. _____ Without power, strength, or the ability to work and function

10. _____ The state of being kept under human control

B. Choose one of the words in the Word Bank above to complete each sentence. Write the word on the line provided.

11. Aaron's parents decided to _____ a tutor to help him with his math.

12. The rumor that the governor was planning to announce her resignation began to
_____ in the capital and then spread around the state.

13. I signed a/an _____ that asked the town to change the laws so people could walk their dogs in the parks.

14. Even though my cat would never hurt a living creature, it didn't take her long to
_____ her toy mouse.

15. Wolves _____ in the wild are often placed in nature reserves.

C. Fill in the bubble next to the answer that best completes the sentence or answers the question.

16. If you are *incapacitated,* you are
    - ○ **A** unable to function
    - ○ **B** held captive
    - ○ **C** not interested
    - ○ **D** undisturbed

17. Read this sentence:

    Organizations exist to encourage the *conservation* of farmland and other open spaces.

    Conservation means
    - ○ **A** development
    - ○ **B** protection
    - ○ **C** destruction
    - ○ **D** recycling

18. When you add your name to a *petition*, you
    - ○ **A** sign a request
    - ○ **B** support a government
    - ○ **C** sign up for a job
    - ○ **D** join an organization

19. People *vegetate* when they
    - ○ **A** don't eat meat
    - ○ **B** admire nature and the outdoors
    - ○ **C** do nothing
    - ○ **D** plant trees and flowers on city streets

20. A *tranquil* environment is
    - ○ **A** calming
    - ○ **B** restrictive
    - ○ **C** confining
    - ○ **D** temporary

21. Read this sentence:

    The activities that you *engage* in during your free time reveal a lot about your interests.

    Engage means
    - ○ **A** observe
    - ○ **B** talk about
    - ○ **C** are enrolled in
    - ○ **D** take part in

22. Animals are kept in *captivity* in a
    - ○ **A** forest
    - ○ **B** zoo
    - ○ **C** park
    - ○ **D** wildlife sanctuary

23. When you describe something *qualitatively,* you tell about its
    - ○ **A** number
    - ○ **B** size
    - ○ **C** characteristics
    - ○ **D** temperature

24. The best synonym for *savage* is
    - ○ **A** untamed
    - ○ **B** find
    - ○ **C** angry
    - ○ **D** eat

25. When the Union army *captured* a city during the Civil War, the soldiers
    - ○ **A** took it by force
    - ○ **B** surrounded the city
    - ○ **C** changed the name
    - ○ **D** gave it away

Food We Can Use

elaborate	fluent	institute	reluctance	unifying
evolve	incline	participatory	sustain	vision

A. From the Word Bank above, choose the word that best matches each meaning. Write the word on the line provided.

1. _____ Ability to perform a skill or speak a language well

2. _____ To put something into effect or introduce or start it

3. _____ A slope

4. _____ Giving people the opportunity to take part

5. _____ To develop or to change and grow

6. _____ To add details or to explain more about something

7. _____ To give support so something can continue

8. _____ Bringing people together in agreement

9. _____ The way a person sees or thinks about things

10. _____ A feeling that causes unwillingness or hesitation

B. Choose one of the words in the Word Bank above to complete each sentence. Write the word on the line provided.

11. I noticed your _____ to apply for the leadership program, and it makes me think you're nervous about being rejected.

12. Mom's _____ has gotten worse as she's aged, so she now wears glasses.

13. When my brother was taking classes at the cooking _____, he made dinner for our family every night.

14. What started out as a simple wedding with just family members turned into a/an _____ affair with more than 200 guests.

15. Working together on a play has had a/an _____ effect on our class.

C. Fill in the bubble next to the answer that best completes the sentence or answers the question.

16. Things *evolve* when they
- **A** spin around
- **B** develop and change
- **C** disappear from view
- **D** grow smaller and less important

17. Read this sentence:

Miriam offered an *elaborate* explanation of why she was late, but none of it was true.

Elaborate means
- **A** detailed
- **B** persuasive
- **C** made up
- **D** sincere

18. One of the five senses, *vision* is the ability to
- **A** feel
- **B** hear
- **C** see
- **D** taste

19. The opposite of *unifying* is
- **A** organizing
- **B** qualifying
- **C** connecting
- **D** dividing

20. If your friends show *reluctance* to go along with your plan, they are
- **A** enthusiastic
- **B** hesitant
- **C** opposed
- **D** without an opinion

21. Read this sentence:

The road's steep *incline* made it difficult for the bicyclist to pedal to the top.

Incline means
- **A** travel
- **B** force
- **C** slope
- **D** impulse

22. When schools *institute* dress codes, they
- **A** make them stricter
- **B** put them into effect
- **C** ask students to wear uniforms
- **D** let students wear what they want

23. Someone who is *fluent* in computer graphics has
- **A** the vocabulary to talk about it
- **B** mastered the skills required
- **C** limited experience in the field
- **D** heard many lectures about it

24. A word closely related to *sustain* is
- **A** assist
- **B** spot
- **C** experience
- **D** struggle

25. When a process is *participatory*, it allows people to
- **A** leave others out
- **B** celebrate
- **C** be the only one
- **D** take part in it

A Female Soldier

ammunition	chasm	emphasize	inherent	parallel
array	drastic	fluctuate	otherwise	repeal

A. From the Word Bank above, choose the word that best matches each meaning. Write the word on the line provided.

1. _____ To stress or give special attention to something

2. _____ Side by side and never meeting

3. _____ Bullets and other explosive devices used in warfare

4. _____ To shift back and forth uncertainly

5. _____ To withdraw or officially do away with a law or policy

6. _____ A division, separation, or difference between people or ideas

7. _____ In a different way or manner

8. _____ Existing by nature

9. _____ Sudden, violent, or extreme

10. _____ A variety or assortment

B. Choose one of the words in the Word Bank above to complete each sentence. Write the word on the line provided.

11. Bing was doing research in the library, gathering _____ to support her position.

12. My mother likes to _____ the importance of good table manners.

13. Even though they lived in different times, the story drew a/an _____ between the composers Bach and Mozart.

14. The best friends agreed to _____ themselves in their dressiest clothes and jewelry for the party.

15. Societies tend to _____ old laws when they become outdated.

C. Fill in the bubble next to the answer that best completes the sentence or answers the question.

16. Another word for *repeal* is
    ○ **A** withdraw
    ○ **B** make
    ○ **C** reapply
    ○ **D** resend

17. Read this sentence:
    At an Indian buffet, you can select from an *array* of curries and other spicy dishes.

    Array means
    ○ **A** assortment
    ○ **B** banquet
    ○ **C** menu
    ○ **D** list

18. If you have the *ammunition* you need for a debate, you have
    ○ **A** experience and practice
    ○ **B** weapons to defend yourself
    ○ **C** facts to support your point
    ○ **D** a large vocabulary

19. A word closely associated with *chasm* is
    ○ **A** split
    ○ **B** cave
    ○ **C** waterfall
    ○ **D** surface

20. Which of these words is NOT a synonym for *inherent*?
    ○ **A** essential
    ○ **B** natural
    ○ **C** inborn
    ○ **D** learned

21. Read this sentence:
    Heinrik doesn't like taking tests, but he is *otherwise* a good student.

    Otherwise means
    ○ **A** in an unusual situation
    ○ **B** under other circumstances
    ○ **C** often
    ○ **D** when paying attention

22. Two streets that are *parallel* do NOT
    ○ **A** have any exits
    ○ **B** have hills
    ○ **C** come together
    ○ **D** go beyond the city boundaries

23. If you take *drastic* measures, you do things that are
    ○ **A** effective
    ○ **B** questionable
    ○ **C** safe
    ○ **D** extreme

24. A synonym for *emphasize* is
    ○ **A** regulate
    ○ **B** exaggerate
    ○ **C** whisper
    ○ **D** stress

25. If prices *fluctuate,* they
    ○ **A** rise continuously
    ○ **B** rise and fall constantly
    ○ **C** stay basically the same
    ○ **D** are set by the sellers

40

Harriet Jacobs

accentuate	distinguished	incentive	prime	recant
disenchanted	flimsy	pledge	prior	sovereign

A. From the Word Bank above, choose the word that best matches each meaning. Write the word on the line provided.

1. _____ A formal promise

2. _____ First in rank or significance

3. _____ To emphasize or intensify

4. _____ Disappointed or dissatisfied

5. _____ Formally or publicly withdraw or take back a statement of belief

6. _____ Independent from the control and influence of others

7. _____ Something that motivates you to do something

8. _____ Lacking strength or substance or made of inferior material

9. _____ Set apart from others

10. _____ Existing from a previous time

B. Choose one of the words in the Word Bank above to complete each sentence. Write the word on the line provided.

11. Mr. Ruiz retired in the _____ of his life and then traveled the world.

12. Queen Beatrix is the _____ of the Netherlands.

13. We _____ money to our community theater every year during its annual fundraising drive.

14. Being healthy should be a strong _____ to eat vitamin-rich food.

15. The mayor's _____ guests included the governor of the state and this year's national gymnastics champion.

C. Fill in the bubble next to the answer that best completes the sentence or answers the question.

16. Which of these is never *sovereign*?
    - ○ **A** a country
    - ○ **B** a street
    - ○ **C** a kingdom
    - ○ **D** a tribe

17. Read this sentence:

    At the start of the school year, Ms. Hayashi makes a *pledge* to her students that she will help them succeed.

    A *pledge* is a

    - ○ **A** promise
    - ○ **B** contract
    - ○ **C** petition
    - ○ **D** speech

18. A *distinguished* person is
    - ○ **A** marked
    - ○ **B** isolated
    - ○ **C** excluded
    - ○ **D** celebrated

19. The opposite of *flimsy* is
    - ○ **A** weak
    - ○ **B** sturdy
    - ○ **C** impossible
    - ○ **D** unlikely

20. If you *recant* a statement you made, you
    - ○ **A** repeat it
    - ○ **B** revise it
    - ○ **C** take it back
    - ○ **D** explain it

21. Read this sentence:

    A Wrinkle in Time is a *prime* example of a book that took a lot of effort to get published.

    Prime means

    - ○ **A** earlier
    - ○ **B** poor
    - ○ **C** excellent
    - ○ **D** famous

22. Someone might *accentuate* her height by wearing
    - ○ **A** baggy jeans
    - ○ **B** a baseball cap
    - ○ **C** a long skirt
    - ○ **D** high-heeled shoes

23. People become *disenchanted* when they
    - ○ **A** have awareness
    - ○ **B** awaken from a dream
    - ○ **C** have been disappointed
    - ○ **D** finish reading a fairy tale

24. A word closely associated with *incentive* is
    - ○ **A** anger
    - ○ **B** motivation
    - ○ **C** movement
    - ○ **D** wealth

25. If you give someone *prior* notice of your vacation plans, you
    - ○ **A** send her the first postcard
    - ○ **B** call her first when you get back
    - ○ **C** call her to say good-bye
    - ○ **D** tell her in advance

Name _____ Date _____ Class _____

President Lincoln Has Died!

brace	commotion	incongruous	psychology	tension
chamber	deceive	portray	scope	via

A. From the Word Bank above, choose the word that best matches each meaning. Write the word on the line provided.

1. _____ The way an individual or a group thinks

2. _____ A room

3. _____ To describe something so that someone can visualize it

4. _____ To prepare for a mental shock or a physical impact

5. _____ A state of disagreement or opposition that exists between two people or two groups

6. _____ The range of activity or influence

7. _____ By way of

8. _____ Noisy, excited confusion

9. _____ To trick or mislead

10. _____ Not suitable to the situation or not harmonious

B. Choose one of the words in the Word Bank above to complete each sentence. Write the word on the line provided.

11. The town's elected officials assembled in the council _____ at City Hall to vote on the proposed law.

12. He paused at the door to _____ things out before entering the room.

13. Heather wears _____ clothes—like cowboy boots with lace dresses.

14. Sayed felt the _____ in the leash as his dog ran after the cat.

15. The bookshelf's _____ was not attached properly to the wall, so the bookshelves and all their contents fell to the floor.

C. Fill in the bubble next to the answer that best completes the sentence or answers the question.

16. When appearances *deceive,* they
    ○ **A** confuse
    ○ **B** mislead
    ○ **C** encourage
    ○ **D** impress

17. Read this sentence:
    Teachers have a good grasp of the *psychology* of their students.

    Psychology means
    ○ **A** the way they think
    ○ **B** their backgrounds
    ○ **C** what they need to learn
    ○ **D** their gender and ethnicity

18. If you go to Seattle *via* Portland, you
    ○ **A** go to Seattle first
    ○ **B** end up in Portland
    ○ **C** avoid Portland
    ○ **D** go to Portland and then Seattle

19. If a character in a story goes to his *chamber,* he is in his
    ○ **A** carriage
    ○ **B** bedroom
    ○ **C** castle
    ○ **D** prison cell

20. The *scope* of a study is its
    ○ **A** introduction
    ○ **B** findings
    ○ **C** range
    ○ **D** authors

21. Read this sentence:
    Dad told us to *brace* ourselves before he announced that we were moving to another state.

    Brace means
    ○ **A** become excited
    ○ **B** hold onto something
    ○ **C** prepare for a surprise
    ○ **D** pack our belongings

22. Screaming and shouting would be *incongruous* behavior at a
    ○ **A** rock concert
    ○ **B** football game
    ○ **C** pep rally
    ○ **D** restaurant

23. When there is *tension* between two groups, there is little
    ○ **A** anger
    ○ **B** understanding
    ○ **C** anticipation
    ○ **D** stress

24. A synonym for *portray* is
    ○ **A** photograph
    ○ **B** enter
    ○ **C** represent
    ○ **D** recount

25. A *commotion* in the library might be caused by
    ○ **A** someone looking for a book
    ○ **B** people logging onto the computers
    ○ **C** people seeing a mouse in the reading room
    ○ **D** librarians discovering a popular new book about bees

44

Final Mastery Test: Part 1

abandon	endeavor	monitor	privilege	retreat
advocate	exploit	moral	perspective	secure
appreciate	gravity	periodical	representation	uniquely

A. From the Word Bank above, choose the word that best matches each meaning. Write the word on the line provided.

1. _____ To use situations or people to your own advantage

2. _____ Appearing from time to time

3. _____ To watch and keep track of what is happening

4. _____ To back off from your position or withdraw from a situation

5. _____ To understand the value, quality, worth, or significance

6. _____ Having to do with right and wrong

7. _____ To object or complain about something

8. _____ Safe and free from danger

9. _____ A special right or a particular advantage

10. _____ A mental point of view

B. Choose one of the words in the Word Bank above to complete each sentence. Write the word on the line provided.

11. Every class in our school has _____ on the student council.

12. Because Nicola's family spoke only German at home, she was _____ qualified to lead the German conversation group at school.

13. We could tell from the _____ in the principal's voice that he was about to tell us something very serious.

14. With total _____, the happy graduates tossed their caps into the air.

15. Many drivers _____ for the development of inexpensive electric cars.

C. Fill in the bubble next to the answer that best completes the sentence or answers the question.

16. The letters that *precede* the letter *V* in the alphabet are
    - ○ **A** *U* and *W*
    - ○ **B** *T* and *U*
    - ○ **C** *W* and *X*
    - ○ **D** *A* and *Z*

17. Read this sentence:
    People often don't see the problems that are *inherent* in their own plans.

    Inherent means:
    - ○ **A** belonging to them by nature
    - ○ **B** resembling their parents
    - ○ **C** very obvious
    - ○ **D** resulting from a surprise

18. Which of the following might be the focus of *conservation*?
    - ○ **A** power plants
    - ○ **B** wilderness areas
    - ○ **C** garbage dumps
    - ○ **D** shopping malls

19. For a comment to be *insightful*, it must
    - ○ **A** focus on the future
    - ○ **B** draw a conclusion
    - ○ **C** describe something
    - ○ **D** show understanding

20. A test that is *comprehensive* covers
    - ○ **A** some of one topic
    - ○ **B** a chapter in a textbook
    - ○ **C** a broad range of information
    - ○ **D** things you haven't learned

21. Read this sentence:
    Many people think that buying a house is a good *investment*.

    Investment means:
    - ○ **A** something that provides hope
    - ○ **B** reason to save money
    - ○ **C** money spent with the expectation of some benefit
    - ○ **D** place to live

22. If you feel *reluctance* about doing something, you are
    - ○ **A** hesitant
    - ○ **B** enthusiastic
    - ○ **C** bored
    - ○ **D** cooperative

23. In a *treacherous* situation, you would be unlikely to feel
    - ○ **A** alert and watchful
    - ○ **B** nervous and uneasy
    - ○ **C** relaxed and safe
    - ○ **D** fearful and concerned

24. The opposite of *accentuate* is
    - ○ **A** highlight
    - ○ **B** emphasize
    - ○ **C** attract
    - ○ **D** minimize

25. Someone tells you a very sad story. An *incongruous* reaction would be to
    - ○ **A** smile sympathetically
    - ○ **B** laugh out loud
    - ○ **C** become tearful
    - ○ **D** say you're sorry

46

Name _____ Date _____ Class _____

Final Mastery Test: Part 2

campaign	contemporary	elaborate	founder	parallel
compound	discrimination	element	intelligence	petition
conclude	distinguished	establish	negative	tension

A. From the Word Bank above, choose the word that best matches each meaning. Write the word on the line provided.

1. _____ To prove an idea, concept, or theory

2. _____ To come together to form a whole

3. _____ A part of a whole or an ingredient

4. _____ Unfavorable or disagreeable

5. _____ To make a decision using reasoning based on information

6. _____ The ability to learn and use your knowledge in new situations

7. _____ A series of actions taken to meet a goal or get a result

8. _____ To make a formal request for something you want or need

9. _____ Side by side and never meeting

10. _____ A state of disagreement between people or groups

B. Choose one of the words in the Word Bank above to complete each sentence. Write the word on the line provided.

11. We watched our puppy take a careful step and then _____ in the snow.

12. Olga shows great _____ when choosing her friends: she spends time only with honest, kind people.

13. Edgar Allan Poe, who was born in 1809, was a/an _____ of Charles Dickens, who was born in 1812.

14. Tariq _____ himself by winning five medals at the track meet.

15. Rhea began sewing the _____ dress three months before the dance.

C. Fill in the bubble next to the answer that best completes the sentence or answers the question.

16. An *episode* in a worker's career might be
    ○ **A** going to work every day
    ○ **B** working extra hours whenever possible
    ○ **C** answering the telephone
    ○ **D** being named "employee of the month"

17. Read this sentence:
    The *administration* of the reading tests will be handled by the language arts teachers.

    Administration means
    ○ **A** scoring
    ○ **B** managing and supervising
    ○ **C** analyzing results
    ○ **D** preparation

18. If you *accelerate* a process, you
    ○ **A** perfect it
    ○ **B** share with others
    ○ **C** speed it up
    ○ **D** increase the work

19. The opposite of *unaffected* is
    ○ **A** candid
    ○ **B** unnatural
    ○ **C** naive
    ○ **D** genuine

20. You might *prioritize* your chores if you had
    ○ **A** very little to do
    ○ **B** unpleasant tasks to do
    ○ **C** many tasks to do
    ○ **D** payment for your work

21. Read this sentence:
    People with a certain type of color blindness cannot *differentiate* between red and green.

    Differentiate means
    ○ **A** use words to describe
    ○ **B** recognize different shades
    ○ **C** see the difference
    ○ **D** name the colors on a color wheel

22. A word closely associated with *prohibit* is
    ○ **A** dwell
    ○ **B** restrict
    ○ **C** demonstrate
    ○ **D** forbid

23. Which of these things would be most *prominent* on a tree in the fall?
    ○ **A** colorful leaves on the branches
    ○ **B** a bird's nest in the treetop
    ○ **C** a squirrel climbing up the trunk
    ○ **D** insects in the bark

24. The opposite of *contradiction* is
    ○ **A** clash
    ○ **B** protest
    ○ **C** agreement
    ○ **D** apology

25. The principal promises to shave his head if everyone in school reads two books over the summer. He hopes this *incentive* will
    ○ **A** be publicity for the school
    ○ **B** amuse the parents
    ○ **C** make students respect him
    ○ **D** encourage the students